TBM/TBF AVENG

in action

By Charles L. Scrivner

Color By Don Greer
Illustrated By Perry Manley

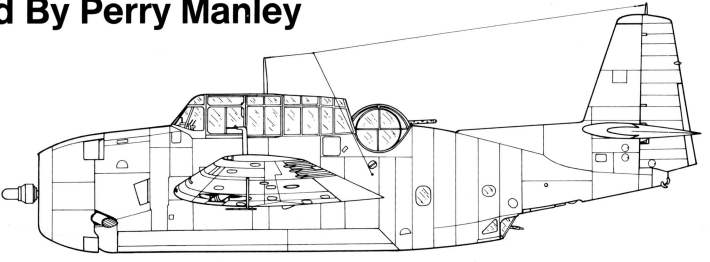

Aircraft Number 82
squadron/signal publications, inc.

(Cover) A TBM-3 Avenger of VT-4 from the USS ESSEX (CV-9), flown by Ensign William H. Cannady, flys through intense anti-aircraft fire to torpedo a Japanese cargo ship of Cap Du San Jacque, French Indo-China on 12 January 1945.

ISBN 0-89747-197-0

If you have any photographs of the aircraft, armor, soldiers or ships of any nation, particularly wartime snapshots, why not share them with us and help make Squadron/Signal's books all the more interesting and complete in the future. Any photograph sent to us will be copied and the original returned. The donor will be fully credited for any photos used. Please send them to:

Squadron/Signal Publications, Inc.
1115 Crowley Drive.
Carrollton, TX 75011-5010.

Acknowledgments

The author expresses his gratitude to many people without whose help this book would have been impossible. Special thanks to my friend CAPT Bill Scarborough, whose urging got it all off high center. To David Lucabaugh, Jim Sullivan, LCDR Bill Cannady and Roger Seybel who offered their photo collections, CDR Lloyd Cole, MAJ John Elliott, USMC (Ret.), the late Richard M Hill, and last but far from least Lois Lovisolo, the Grumman Historian, who endured a barrage of questions and requests for material.

A common sight in the Pacific Theater during 1943, a TBF-1C Avenger on an anti-submarine patrol ahead of a Navy task force. The antenna under the port wing is for the Air to Surface type B (ASB) radar and the inverted 'L' shaped device on the wingtip is the pitot tube. (Grumman)

2

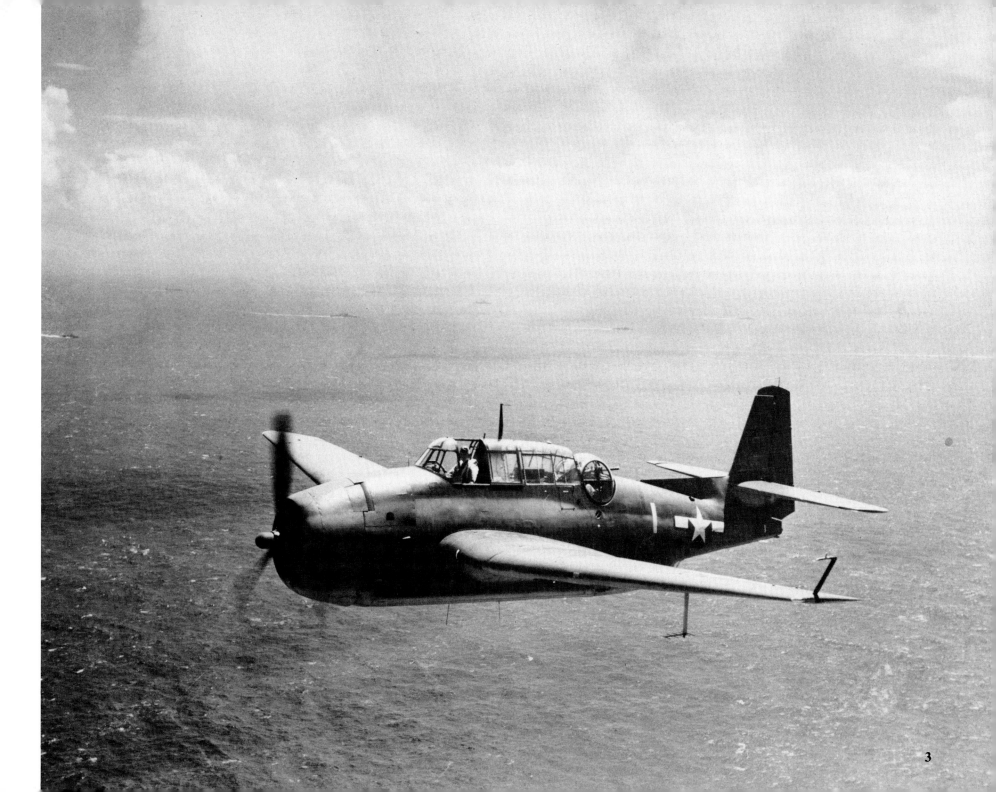

Introduction

During 1939 the United States Navy began an ambitious program to both modernize and increase the size of its carrier fleet. New aircraft to equip the carrier squadrons being formed were in production with the F4F Wildcat fighter and SBD Dauntlesss dive bomber entering service with VF (fighter) and VSB (Scout-bomber) squadrons. Additionally, more advanced replacements for these aircraft (F4U Corsair, F6F Hellcat and SB2C Helldiver) had been designed and were in now in prototype testing. Only in the VT (torpedo bomber) class had development failed to keep pace with Navy VT squadrons being still equipped with the Douglas TBD-1 Devastator, which had entered service in 1937. The Navy recognized that the Devastator could not be further developed to overcome its two major drawbacks, insufficient speed and short range. An entirely new aircraft was needed. The German invasion of Poland and Japanese aggression in China underscored the urgency for replacing the Devastator with a more combat capable torpedo bomber.

During October of 1939, the Navy issued a request for proposals to the US aviation industry for a new torpedo bomber to replace the Devastator. The Navy's requirements included: a three man crew, a top speed of 300 mph, an internal bomb bay with a capacity of one torpedo or three 500 pound bombs, self-sealing fuel tanks, armor protection, and a powered dorsal gun turret. A number of companies submitted proposals but only two designs, one by the Chance Vought Company and one by the Grumman Aircraft Engineering Company were considered for experimental contracts. During April of 1940 the Navy contracted for two experimental prototypes from each company, designating the Chance Vought design the XTBU-1 and the Grumman design the XTBF-1.

Grumman had never before designed a torpedo bomber, but had been one of the Navy's primary suppliers of carrier based fighter aircraft, from the FF-1 biplane through the F4F Wildcat. With time a critical factor, the Grumman engineering team relied heavily on engineering data already proven during the development of Grumman's first monoplane fighter the F4F-4 Wildcat. As the torpedo bomber design evolved, it began to take a strong family resemblance to its stablemate, the Wildcat.

Like the Wildcat, the XTBF-1 was a radial engined, all metal, mid-wing monoplane with a deep oval tapering fuselage. The deep fuselage allowed room for an internal bomb bay under the wing center section and a lower rear defensive gun position immediately behind the bomb bay. The internal bomb bay was a new feature for naval bombers and Grumman's design exceeded the Navy's requirements, being capable of accommodating a 2,000 pound torpedo or four 500 pound bombs. The three man crew, pilot, radioman, and gunner would be housed under a long greenhouse canopy that ended with a dorsal powered turret. Entry to the rear fuselage position could be made from either the rear cockpit or through a door in the starboard fuselage side.

The most difficult part of the Navy specification was the requirement for a powered dorsal gun turret. The weight and slow traverse of early mechanical and hydraulic gun turrets had made installation on single engine aircraft impractical and Grumman's approach to the problem was both unique and innovative. Grumman engineer, Oscar Olsen, applied the principal used on large industrial electric motors called *Amplidynes** to design an electrically driven ball turret. Working with General Electric engineers, Olsen developed small versions of the Amplidyne motor that could be synchronized with each other to drive the turret in both traverse and elevation. When these new motors were tested on the turret prototype, they proved so successful that the turret/motor combination was approved for mass production without modification.

An Amplidyne electric motor is a motor-generator combination which maintains speed under a load, allowing precision control of both the torque and speed of the motor.

A Douglas TBD-1 Devastator of VT-3, the first squadron to receive the Devastator during 1937. The Devastator was already obsolete by the time it saw combat and Devastator squadrons were destroyed at the Battle of Midway, losing thirty-nine of the forty-one aircraft that attacked the Japanese carriers. (CAPT W.E. Scarborough)

The Vought XTBU-1 Sea Wolf was the XTBF-1s rival for the Navy torpedo bomber contract. Vought was heavily committed to development of the F4U Corsair and the TBU design was sold to Consolidated. In the event only 189 would be produced under the designation TBY-2 before the war ended. Two Squadrons equipped with TBY-2s were preparing to deploy overseas on V-J Day. (Don Bratt)

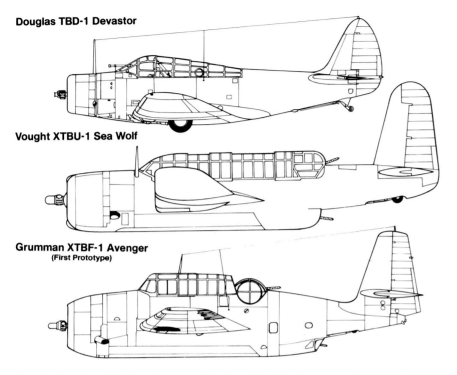

Douglas TBD-1 Devastor

Vought XTBU-1 Sea Wolf

Grumman XTBF-1 Avenger
(First Prototype)

Fitted with a dorsal fin fillet to improve directional stability, the second XTBF-1 (BuNO 2540) prototype undergoes ground engine checks just prior to its first flight on 15 December 1941. Within a month of this first flight, the first production TBF-1 would roll off the Grumman production line at Bethpage, Long Island. (Grumman)

Olsen's ball turret was a self-contained unit with the gun, gunner, controls and ammunition all within the plexiglas ball turret mounted at the rear of the greenhouse. The gunner sat alongside the single .50 caliber machine gun in an armored seat protected by half inch armor plate mounted on the turret front and sides, quarter inch armor plate under the seat and an inch and a half armored glass panel directly in front of him. The turret controls were both simple and reliable, a single pistol grip handle controlled the turret's elevation, traverse, and had a trigger for firing the gun. Two gunsights were installed, the standard Navy Mk 9 reflector sight and a Mk 11 ring and post sight as a back-up. The turret was entered from below through the radioman's station and once inside, the gunner secured the hinged seat under him. In an emergency the gunner could quickly escape from the turret either by removing the emergency exit hatch on the starboard side of the turret or through the lower fuselage door at the radioman's station.

At Bethpage, Long Island, construction of the two Grumman XTBF-1 prototypes progressed quickly. Based on data obtained from the XTBF-1 mock-up the Navy, during December of 1940, ordered 286 aircraft under the designation TBF-1. Internal equipment changes ordered by the Navy increased the weight of the prototype by 1,000 pounds and the projected top speed fell under the required 300 mph. The first TBF-1 (BuNo 2539), powered by a 1,700 hp Wright R-2600-8 Cyclone engine driving a Hamilton-Standard variable pitch propeller made its first official flight on 7 August 1941. The first prototype was fitted with a large angular fin and rudder at the extreme end of the gracefully tapering rear fuselage, but early in the prototype flight test program, problems with lateral stability led to a re-design of the fin and rudder. A long fin fillet was added to the fin leading edge, smoothly fairing in the fin with the fuselage and providing the XTBF-1 the extra side area needed to improve stability.

The outwardly retracting landing gear, folding outer wing panels, flaps and bomb bay doors were all hydraulically operated. Grumman designed the wings to fold back laterally along the fuselage sides to alleviate the height problem that conventional upward folding wings would have caused on carrier hangar decks. The powered folding wings could be folded or unfolded by the pilot in seconds and required no assistance from ground crews. The smaller overall size of the XTBF-1 with the wings folded was one of the deciding factors that won Grumman the Navy torpedo bomber contract over the Vought XTBU-1.

The XTBF-1 carried a defensive armament of one .50 caliber machine gun with 400 rounds in the turret, a .30 caliber machine gun with 300 rounds of ammunition fixed in the upper starboard side of the cowling and fired by the pilot, and a .30 caliber machine gun with 500 rounds mounted in a lower fuselage 'stinger' position manned by the radioman. The large internal bomb bay under the wing center section had a maximum capacity of 2,000 pounds and could carry, bombs, torpedos, depth charges, mines or a special jettisonable 270 gallon fuel tank. With the bomb bay fuel tank installed the XTBF-1 had a maximum range of 2,180 miles, ideal for long range reconnaissance missions. For dive bombing missions, the main landing gear could be used as dive brakes and could be extended in flight at speeds up to 200 mph. The tailhook was installed at the extreme rear of the fuselage and was fully retractable.

Grumman's flight test program progressed smoothly and the prototype demonstrated a top speed of 271 mph, a rate of climb of 1,430 feet per minute, a ceiling of 22,400 feet, and a normal range of 1,215 miles. On 28 November the program suffered a setback when an in-flight fire in the bomb bay forced Grumman test pilot Hobart Cook and engineer Gordon Israel to abandon the prototype. Fortunately, the second XTBF-1 (BuNo 2540) was nearly complete and by working around the clock, the second prototype was finished in three weeks allowing the flight test program to proceed on schedule. The second prototype made its first flight on 15 December 1941, and coming so soon after the Japanese attack on Pearl Harbor was christened the Avenger. Flight testing continued with the second XTBF-1 until 23 December 1941 when the Navy officially accepted the XTBF-1 and changed the production contract from 286 aircraft to an open ended production contract.

5

Development

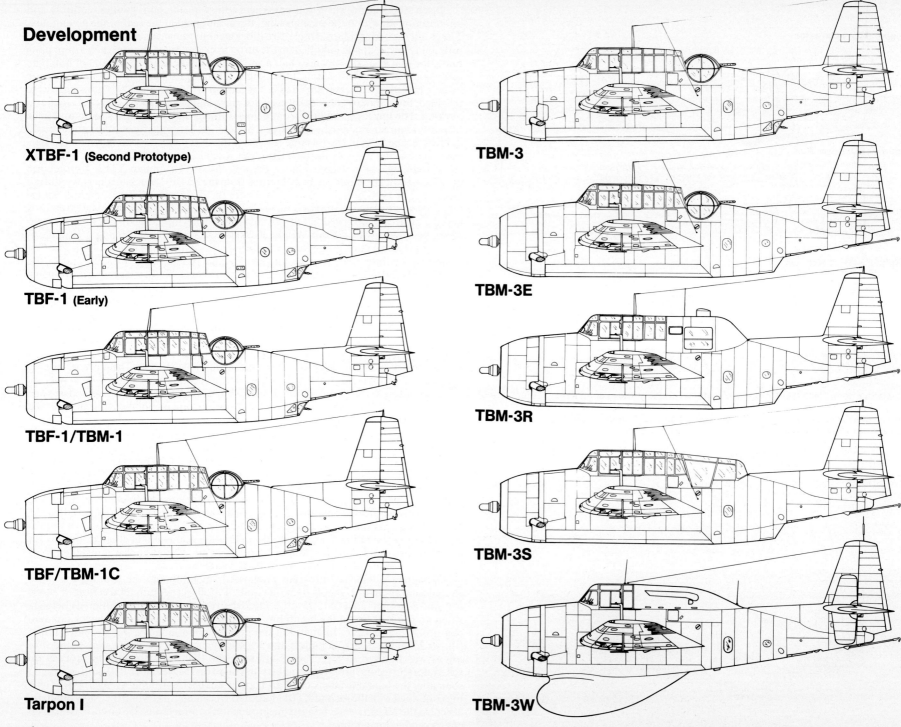

XTBF-1 (Second Prototype)

TBF-1 (Early)

TBF-1/TBM-1

TBF/TBM-1C

Tarpon I

TBM-3

TBM-3E

TBM-3R

TBM-3S

TBM-3W

TBF-1

Early production TBF-1s were identical to the second XTBF-1 prototype with the dorsal fin fillet. As a safety measure, the first fifty TBF-1s were equipped with a second set of flight controls in the rear cockpit. These proved to be impractical and were deleted with the fifty-first production aircraft. To improve visibility from the radioman's station, the windows on the port fuselage side were reconfigured on later TBF-1s, and the two small windows (one rectangular and one circular) on the port side were replaced by an larger oval window even with the trailing edge of the wing. Radar was introduced on the Avenger during the first year of production and a yagi antenna mast for Air to Surface type B radar (ASB) was installed under each wing on the outer wing panels. The radar scope and controls were mounted in the radioman's station and the ASB became the standard radar fitted to all Avengers.

The first production TBF-1 rolled off the Grumman assembly line on 3 January 1942 and after company tests and acceptance flights were completed the aircraft was officially delivered to the Navy on 30 January. Five additional Avengers were delivered during February and these first six production aircraft were ferried to Naval Air Station Norfolk, Virginia where the first Navy Avenger squadron was being formed.

A detachment of twenty-one aircrews from USS HORNET's Torpedo Squadron Eight (VT-8) under the command of the squadron's Executive Officer, LT H.H. Larson were at Norfolk to accept the Avengers and begin training with their new mounts. HORNET had sailed from Norfolk for the Pacific in February of 1942, with the remainder of the squadron and fifteen TBD-1 Devastators. Orders were left for the Avenger detachment to complete their training and rejoin HORNET as soon as possible. Unfortunately a delay was encountered when the first six TBF-1s had to be returned to Grumman during March for installation of new wing fold hinge pins.

The VT-8 detachment completed their training in record time and on 8 May 1942 ferried their Avengers cross-country to San Diego, California. At San Diego the Avengers were loaded aboard the aircraft transport USS KITTY HAWK (APV-1) and

An early production TBF-1 (BuNo 00373) undergoes acceptance trials at NAS Anacostia, Washington D.C. on 23 March 1942. The first fifty TBF-1s were equipped with emergency flight controls in the rear cockpit, but these were deleted beginning with the 51st production machine. (USN via David Lucabaugh)

sailed for Pearl Harbor, arriving on 29 May, the day after the HORNET sailed for Midway. Shortly after their arrival on Ford Island, Pearl Harbor, volunteers were requested to fly six of the Avengers to reinforce Midway — all twenty-one aircrews volunteered. Six were chosen and VT-8 (Midway Detachment) under the command of LT L.K. Fieberling departed for the eight hour flight to the island on 1 June 1942. The other five pilots of the detachment were; Ensigns C.E. Brannon, A.K. Earnest, O.J. Gaunier, V.A. Lewis, and enlisted Naval Air Pilot AMM1c (NAP) D.D. Woodside.

Shortly after daylight on 4 June 1942, a PBY Catalina flying boat located the Japanese invasion fleet headed for Midway and at 0545 the six torpedo armed TBF-1s were ordered into the air. The Avengers climbed to 4,000 feet and headed for the Japanese fleet, sighting their targets at about 0710. ENS Earnest, from his vantage point in '8-T-1', could see the Japanese carriers, screened by battleships, cruisers and destroyers. The Avenger formation quickly came under attack when they were intercepted by A6M2 Zero fighters from the Japanese combat air patrol. The unescorted TBFs dived for the water and continued toward the enemy fleet at 150 feet. '8-T-1' was not damaged in the first fighter attack, but during the running fight that followed, a Zero hit the turret, killing the gunner, J.D. Manning. The radioman, Harry Farrier, was hit and briefly knocked unconscious and Earnest was also slightly wounded as the Zeros continued their relentless attacks.

Still several miles from the enemy carriers Earnest saw the other two Avengers of his three plane section crash into the water, shot down by Japanese fighters. Another Zero attacked 8-T-1 and the elevator cables were severed. The TBF headed for the water and in desperation Earnest dropped his torpedo at what he thought was a cruiser. In an attempt to halt the Avengers descent Earnest applied full up elevator trim and the TBF slowly climbed and remained airborne. Guided by the smoke from Midway's burning fuel tanks Earnest flew back to Midway and made a one-wheel, crash landing on the beach. Earnest and Farrier climbed from the bullet riddled TBF-1 — the only survivors of the six VT-8 Avengers. It had been an inauspicious combat debut for the Avenger.

During the sixty day period between the Battle of Midway and the beginning of the Guadalcanal campaign all carrier based torpedo squadrons were re-equipped with TBF-1 Avengers and the TBD-1 Devastator passed into history.

Tail Development

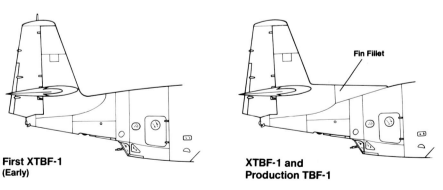

First XTBF-1 (Early)

Fin Fillet

XTBF-1 and Production TBF-1

A Navy ferry crew prepares to board a new production TBF-1 for delivery to Torpedo Squadron Eight (VT-8) at Naval Air Station Norfolk, Virginia. VT-8 was the first Navy squadron to receive the Avenger and would give the TBF its baptism of fire at the Battle of Midway. (Grumman)

A ship's crane lifts a TBF-1 from the dock to the hangar deck of a Pacific carrier during 1942. When level with the deck edge, the Avenger will be swung tail first through the open hangar bay hatch. The crewman riding in the cockpit is the aircraft's plane captain who will control the brakes as the aircraft is moved into position within the hangar deck. (USN via MAJ J.M. Elliott, USMC-Ret.)

Grumman 150SE Turret

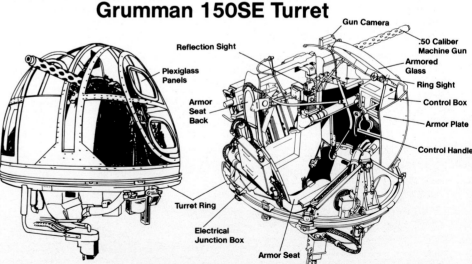

ENS A.K. Earnest managed to successfully crash land his TBF-1 (8-T-1) on Midway Island with his elevator controls shot away and his crew either dead or wounded. 8-T-1 was the only VT-8 Avenger to return from the six aircraft that began the squadron's attack on the Japanese fleet. (Grumman)

The pilots cockpit and instrument panel of a TBF-1. Primary flight instruments are grouped on the center panel, while engine instruments are grouped on the lower starboard and port side panels. (Grumman)

Port side of the pilots cockpit of a TBF-1. The cockpit interior was painted Zink Chromate Green primer on the bulkheads with Instrument Black on the control and instrument panels.

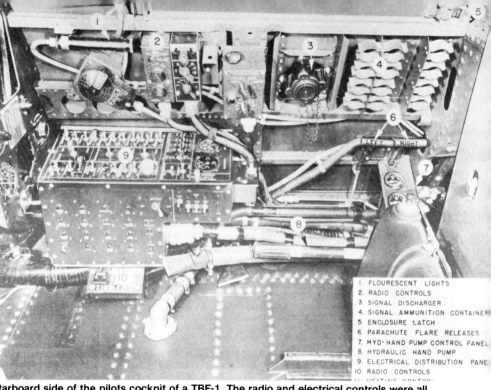

1. FLOURESCENT LIGHTS
2. RADIO CONTROLS
3. SIGNAL DISCHARGER
4. SIGNAL AMMUNITION CONTAINER
5. ENCLOSURE LATCH
6. PARACHUTE FLARE RELEASES
7. HYD-HAND PUMP CONTROL PANEL
8. HYDRAULIC HAND PUMP
9. ELECTRICAL DISTRIBUTION PANE
10. RADIO CONTROLS
11. HEATING CONTROL

Starboard side of the pilots cockpit of a TBF-1. The radio and electrical controls were all grouped on the starboard cockpit bulkhead. The signal discharger (3) for a Very flare pistol was used in signaling the carrier during periods of radio silence.

During 1942 the Navy experimented with the use of small tractors to move the large TBF-1s on carrier decks. The tests centered on handling and maneuverability of the tractors compared with the usual method of manually moving the aircraft around the flight deck. (USN via MAJ J.M. Elliott, USMC-Ret.)

1. EMERGENCY ENCLOSURE RELEASE
2. MAP CASE
3. FUEL SYSTEM DIAGRAM
4. TAIL WHEEL CASTER LOCK
5. S.B.A.E. ATTITUDE CONTROL
6. EMERGENCY ELEC. FUEL PUMP SWITCH
7. MIXTURE CONTROL
8. THROTTLE CONTROL
9. SUPERCHARGER CONTROL
10. CONTROL QUADRANT FRICTION ADJUSTMENT
11. RUDDER TAB CONTROL
12. AILERON TAB CONTROL
13. ELEVATOR TAB CONTROL
14. ARRESTING HOOK SWITCH
15. OXYGEN PLUG-IN
16. FLAP & LANDING GEAR CONTROL UNIT
17. LANDING GEAR EMERGENCY RELEASE

With wheels, flaps, and tail hook down a TBF-1 goes around after receiving a 'wave-off' from the carrier LSO (Landing Signal Officer). Because of its size the Avenger was often referred to by the nickname 'Turkey'. During the Second World War the term 'turkey' meant simply — 'a big bird!'. (Grumman)

The two antennas mounted on the inboard edge of the national insignia are yagi antennas for the ASB radar. The TBF main landing gear wheel wells deliberately lacked covers, because Grumman engineers thought wheel well doors were unnecessary weight and would further increase maintenance difficulties. (Grumman)

Air To Surface Type B Radar (ASB)

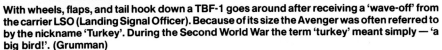

Moveable antenna mounted under each wing

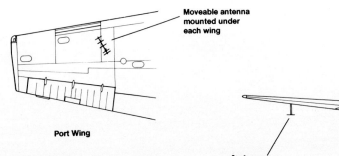

Port Wing

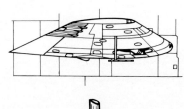

Antenna   Antenna

A pair of TBF-1s of an Operational Training Squadron pass over the wake of a submarine's periscope (just behind the tail of the lead Avenger) while conducting anti-submarine training off Florida's east coast during early 1943. The pilots canopy has a slot at the top for the radio antenna mast. (Grumman)

A TBF-1 undergoing preflight engine run-up at NAS San Diego, California. With the wings folded the TBF's wingspan was reduced from 54 feet 2 inches to 19 feet. The aircraft's side number (160) is repeated on the wing leading edges in Black. (Grumman)

The crew of this TBF-1 on Munda Island has painted 'guns' on the wing leading edge in an effort to convince the enemy that the Avenger was armed with six machine guns. On 29 June 1943 the US national insignia was changed from the circle and star to the star and bar. Squadrons were slow to implement the change and some six months later, on 6 December 1943, these TBF are carrying a mixture of markings. (USN via David Lucabaugh)

A wildly maneuvering Japanese ASASHIO class destroyer under attack by an Avenger during the 16 February 1944 raid on Truk Island. The Avenger has scored a hit and Japanese destroyer's back has been broken with its stern severed just aft of the stack. (Grumman)

This early production TBF-1 on the ramp at Bethpage has been fitted with a non-standard cuffed propeller. The normal propeller used with the 1,700 hp Wright R-2600-B engine was the Hamilton Standard constant speed, full feathering propeller. (Grumman)

The US Navy operated two side paddle wheel aircraft carriers on Lake Michigan during the Second World War. Both USS WOLVERINE and USS SABLE were training carriers converted from Great Lakes cruise ships. ENS W.D. Henderson nosed over this overall Glossy Sea Blue TBF-1 during Carrier Qualifications (CARQUALS) aboard USS SABLE on 2 August 1945. (Smithsonian via F.C. Durant)

Port Side Radioman's Windows

TBF-1 (Early)

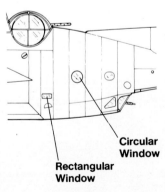

Circular Window

Rectangular Window

TBF-1 (Late)

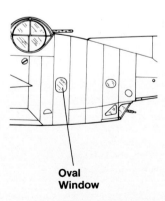

Oval Window

Eastern Aircraft TBM-1

By late June 1942, Grumman was building sixty TBF-1s per month, but the Navy desperately needed more Avengers than Grumman was able to manufacture. At the time Grumman was also heavily engaged in production of the F4F Wildcat and was tooling-up to build the next generation of Navy fighter — the F6F-3 Hellcat. The Navy decided that production of the F6F Hellcat should have top priority and sought to have production of both the F4F-4 Wildcat and TBF-1 Avenger subcontracted to another manufacturer.

During late 1941, the US government had ordered civilian automobile production drastically curtailed. When war was declared on 8 December 1941, the General Motors Corporation ceased all automobile production, idling five huge auto plants. The General Motors management felt that these idle plants could be put to use in the war effort and began seeking contracts to manufacture spare parts for existing aircraft designs.

During early 1942 the Navy Department arranged a meeting between General Motors and Grumman. The General Motors (GM) representatives thought Grumman was seeking a supplier for spare parts, but were shocked to find that Grumman actually wanted additional factory space for full scale aircraft production. GM engineers visited Grumman to study aircraft production techniques and Grumman engineers traveled to GM plants to assist in the enormous job of revamping the automobile plants for aircraft production. By mid-1942 all five GM plants had been completely reorganized, becoming the Eastern Aircraft Division of the General Motors Corporation.

Under the terms of the agreement between the Navy, Grumman and Eastern Aircraft, Eastern would receive twenty sets of sub-assemblies (ten F4F Wildcat fighters and ten TBF Avenger bombers), as well as specially configured 'PK' aircraft to be used as training aids. The 'PK' aircraft were standard F4F-4 and TBF-1 aircraft assembled with Parker-Kalon (PK) fasteners instead of rivets. These aircraft could be easily disassembled and assembled for study.

Eastern's Trenton, New Jersey plant was assigned to build the TBF-1 Avenger under the designation TBM-1 Avenger while the Linden, New Jersey plant would build the F4F-4 Wildcat under the designation FM-1 Wildcat. The Tarrytown, Bloomfield and Baltimore plants would build components and subassemblies for both. Eastern Aircraft delivered its first TBM-1, assembled from parts supplied by Grumman, during November of 1942 with two more TBM-1s delivered in December (also built from Grumman supplied sub-assemblies). By March of 1943 Eastern had begun building its own assemblies, completing thirty-one TBM-1s. Grumman was now free to concentrate on production of the Hellcat.

Eastern Aircraft (GM) produced TBM-1 Avengers and Grumman produced TBF-1 Avengers were virtually identical and could not be differentiated except by comparing the BuNo.

Eastern Aircraft rapidly increased TBM production, delivering seventy-five Avengers during June and 100 in July. In November of 1943 production had reached 215 TBMs per month and by 1945 Eastern had reached a phenomenal 350 aircraft per month. The record month for TBM production was March of 1945, when Eastern built 400 aircraft in a single thirty day period.

Grumman continued to build TBF-1s until December of 1943, at which time TBF production at Bethpage ended (after producing 2,291 aircraft), with Grumman having shifted to full scale production of the F6F-3 Hellcat. From December of 1943 Eastern Aircraft became the sole manufacturer of Avengers, and would build a total of 7,546 TBMs before the end of the war, 77 percent of all Avenger production.

The Eastern Aircraft Division of General Motors began building the Avenger under the designation TBM during late 1942. An early production TBM-1 prepares for take-off on its acceptance flight from the Eastern Aircraft plant at Linden, New Jersey. Eastern would eventually build over 7,000 Avengers before the war ended. (Bob Gilbert)

A TBM-1 (BuNo 24737) is positioned on the catapult aboard the escort carrier USS MISSION BAY (CVE-59) during the carrier's Atlantic shakedown cruise in November of 1943. The national insignia has the thin Red border used between June 1943 and October of 1943. (USN via David Lucabaugh)

(Above) A TBM-1 of VT-51 from USS SAN JACINTO (CVL-30) enroute to targets on Peleliu on 16 September 1944. TBM-1s armed with bombs were often used to support ground troops during the island hopping campaign of the Pacific War. (USN via David Lucabaugh)

(Below) This battle damaged TBM-1 made a successful belly landing on Baknika Island in the Russells Group on 27 June 1944. Fearing fire, the turret gunner has jettisoned the emergency turret hatch and made a quick escape from the Avenger. (USN via David Lucabaugh)

This TBM-1 nosed over during night carrier qualifications aboard USS BATAAN (CVL-29) on 3 February 1944 damaging the starboard wing. Light carriers normally operated a squadron of fighters and a squadron of Avengers. Later in the war Avengers flying from USS BATAAN would score four torpedo hits on the Japanese battleship YAMOTO, the worlds most heavily armed warship. (USN via David Lucabaugh)

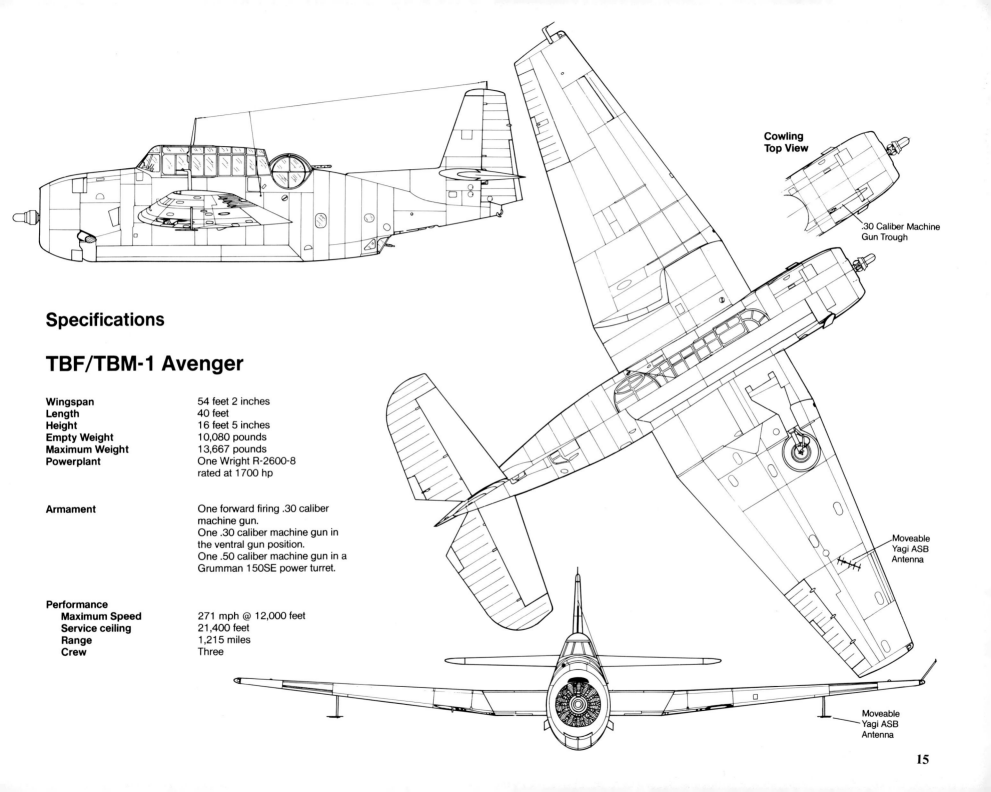

**Cowling
Top View**

.30 Caliber Machine
Gun Trough

Specifications

TBF/TBM-1 Avenger

Wingspan	54 feet 2 inches
Length	40 feet
Height	16 feet 5 inches
Empty Weight	10,080 pounds
Maximum Weight	13,667 pounds
Powerplant	One Wright R-2600-8
	rated at 1700 hp
Armament	One forward firing .30 caliber
	machine gun.
	One .30 caliber machine gun in
	the ventral gun position.
	One .50 caliber machine gun in a
	Grumman 150SE power turret.
Performance	
Maximum Speed	271 mph @ 12,000 feet
Service ceiling	21,400 feet
Range	1,215 miles
Crew	Three

Moveable
Yagi ASB
Antenna

Moveable
Yagi ASB
Antenna

TBF/TBM-1C

It quickly became obvious to Navy aircrews flying the Avenger in combat that the forward firepower of the single cowl mounted .30 machine gun was totally inadequate. The need for additional forward firepower led the ordnancemen of Torpedo Squadron Ten (VT-10) to install a .50 machine gun, ammunition and interuptor gear *externally on* each wingroot of the commanding officer's TBF-1. This field modification proved successful and the design was forwarded to Bethpage by a Grumman tech rep in Hawaii. The Grumman Engineering Department refined VT-10's design so that the guns could be mounted internally in each wing outside the propeller arc eliminating the need for interuptor gears.

This modification consisted of reinforcing the TBF-1's wing structure to accept the added weight and recoil of the heavy Browning machine gun, installing a gun mount in each wing just outboard the wing fold, and mounting an ammunition box for 600 rounds outboard of the gun. The .30 caliber cowling machine gun was deleted and the cowling reconfigured to eliminate the gun trough. The radio mast on top of the canopy was repositioned further back on the canopy and the antenna lead-in was moved to the fuselage side below the turret. The new wing was introduced into production on 12 July 1943 and aircraft carrying this modification were designated TBF-1Cs (the TBF-1B was the Navy designation for lend-lease Avengers supplied to the British). When Eastern Aircraft incorporated the wing gun modification into the TBM-1 production line at Trenton these aircraft were designated TBM-1Cs. The TBF/TMB-1C first entered squadron service in late 1943 and provided Avenger crews the increased forward firepower needed to suppress enemy anti-aircraft fire.

Eastern Aircraft (GM) produced TBM-1C Avengers and Grumman produced TBF-1C Avengers were identical and could not be differentiated except by comparing the BuNo.

Unfortunately other problems with Avenger armament were not so easily solved. The standard Navy aerial torpedo, the Mk 13, was slow and unreliable, and too often Avenger pilots were frustrated in their attacks against enemy shipping by malfunctioning torpedos. The Mk-13 was limited to drops from less than 100 feet and at airspeeds of under 100 knots, putting Avenger crews at great risk from a targets anti-aircraft batteries. The slow speed of the Mk 13 also made it easy for fast warships to evade a torpedo attack.

This pair of TBM-1Cs of VT-7 carry the White 'horseshoe' identification marking carried by aircraft assigned to USS HANCOCK (CV-19). The White square on the wing leading edge is tape covering the blast tubes of the wing .50 caliber machine guns. The wing guns on the TBF/TBM-1C were mounted just outboard of the wing fold and the cowl mounted .30 machine gun was deleted. (USN via David Lucabaugh)

A TBM-1C of VC-30 is catapulted from the deck of USS MONTEREY (CVL-26) during 1943. Heavily loaded Avengers usually settled after leaving the deck until they built up enough airspeed to begin their climb to altitude. (Hank Weimer Collection via Jim Sullivan)

Cowling

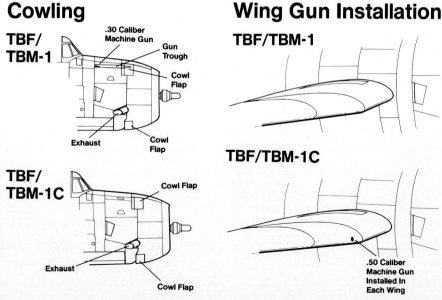

TBF/ TBM-1
.30 Caliber Machine Gun
Gun Trough
Cowl Flap
Exhaust
Cowl Flap

TBF/ TBM-1C
Cowl Flap
Exhaust
Cowl Flap

Wing Gun Installation

TBF/TBM-1

TBF/TBM-1C
.50 Caliber Machine Gun Installed In Each Wing

Early attempts to improve the Mk-13 torpedo's performance included fitting the Mk-13 with a plywood box-like tail fin that added stability during the drop and broke away on impact with the water. A plywood nose drag ring was also fitted which improved the torpedo's flight attitude during free fall and cushioned the torpedo's water entry before it too broke away. These improvements were, however, only stop-gap measures and it was not until the California Institute of Technology devised a ten inch tail shroud ring welded to the torpedo's fins that the torpedo's reliability improved. The revised torpedo was designated the Mk-13-1A and quickly became known to Avenger crews as the 'ring-tailed' torpedo. The improved flight characterizes of the 'ring-tailed' torpedo now allowed drops from up to 800 feet and at airspeeds of 280 knots, greatly increasing the Avengers chances of survival during a torpedo attack against a heavily armed enemy ship

While problems with the torpedos were worked out, Avenger's were being used more often as glide and skip bombers than as torpedo bombers. Internal bomb loads varied according to the mission, and the Avenger was found to be well suited for carrying a variety of weapons. The internal bomb bay was capable of housing one 2000 pound GP (General Purpose) bomb, or one 1600 pound AP (Armor Piercing) bomb. Alternate loads consisted of two 1000 pound GP bombs, four 500 pound GP bombs, twelve 100 pound GP bombs or four 350 pound Depth Bombs.

When attacking a maneuvering ship at sea, Avenger tactics called for dropping a 'stick' of up to four bombs using a intervalometer which controlled the spread (spacing) of the bombs. The intervalometer was mounted in the radioman's station and the Avenger's airspeed and the desired bomb spacing was set by the radioman. The target was attacked in a 30 to 45 degree dive to an altitude of 500 feet or lower. The pilot released the bombs as he leveled off and the intervalometer would space the bombs 60 to 75 feet apart, practically guaranteeing one or more hits on the target from a stick of four bombs. These tactics proved highly successful and the Avenger gained a reputation as a highly accurate bombing platform.

(Right) An Avenger of Torpedo Squadron Four (VT-4) aboard USS Ranger (CV-4) drops a Mk 13 torpedo while on a training exercise during 1942. The white smoke plume behind the torpedo's tail is the motor's steam exhaust. Mk 13 torpedos were unreliable and it was not until late in the war that more improved torpedos were available to Avenger squadrons. (Grumman)

(Below) Navy Ordnancemen wheel a Mk 13 Aircraft Torpedo to a waiting Avenger at a stateside Naval Air Station. The box-like plywood auxiliary tail fins were designed to give the torpedo added stability during the drop and brake away on impact with the water. (Grumman)

Aerial Torpedos

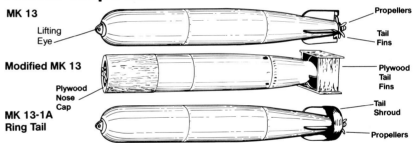

MK 13 — Lifting Eye, Propellers, Tail Fins

Modified MK 13 — Plywood Nose Cap, Plywood Tail Fins

MK 13-1A Ring Tail — Tail Shroud, Propellers

Three TBF-1s practice the classic torpedo bomber attack, a straight in, low altitude torpedo drop. The Mk 13 torpedo was limited to drops from less than 100 feet and speeds under 100 knots. During a torpedo attack, one section of Avengers would approach the target from one direction while a second section attacked from the opposite side, in what was known as an 'anvil' attack. (Grumman)

Ordnancemen load 500 pound GP bombs into the bomb bay of an Avenger with a Mk 7 Bomb Hoist. After the bombs are shackled in place, fuses and arming wires will be installed and the bomb bay doors closed. A normal bomb load for the Avenger was four 500 pound bombs. (Grumman)

Navy Ordnancemen assemble Incendiary Clusters (fire bombs) in preparation for a mission against Tarawa Atoll during September of 1943. Each incendiary cluster contained thirty-four Thermite/Magnesium bomblets which when dropped would open and spread the bomblets over a wide area. (Grumman)

The bomb bay of an Avenger loaded with 500 pound practice bombs. Two additional 500 pound bombs could be loaded for a total bomb load of 2,000 pounds. The window at the rear of the bomb bay is a sighting window for the bombardier. (Grumman)

Groundcrews on Guadalcanal prepare to load a train of 500 pound GP bombs on an Avenger during 1942. The bombs are fully armed with both nose and tail fuses in place. Navy and Marine Avengers on Guadalcanal were used as glide bombers against Japanese shipping attempting to land reinforcements on the island. (Grumman)

Ordnancemen aboard USS FANSHAW BAY (CVE-70) wheel Mk 54 flat-nose depth bombs across the deck past a TBM-1C of VC-68 during October of 1944. The White diamond on the Avenger's rudder was the squadron identification marking for VC-68. (Richard M. Hill)

MK 54
Depth
Bomb

Seconds from impact, this TBM-1C of VC-65 went over the side of USS SAINT LO (CVE-63) on 27 June 1944. USS SAINT LO was the first *Kamikaze* loss during the Battle of Leyte Gulf, when a Japanese suicide aircraft penetrated her flight deck and exploded in the bomb magazine. (USN via David Luca-baugh)

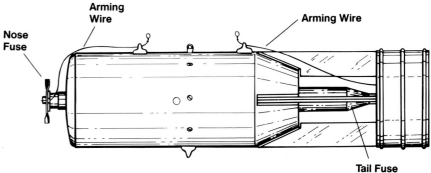

Nose Fuse

Arming Wire

Arming Wire

Tail Fuse

19

1. BOMBER'S ELECTRICAL PANEL
2. SENDING KEY
3. ALTIMETER
4. OUTSIDE AIR TEMP. GAGE
5. TURN AND BANK INDICATOR
6. RELIEF TUBE
7. CATAPULT HAND GRIPS
8. BOMB DOOR CONTROL
9. OXYGEN SPARE CANISTER RACK
10. 30 CAL. AMMUNITION CONTAINER
11. EMERGENCY DOOR RELEASE
12. BOMB SIGHT

The radioman's station of an Avenger looking forward. The Norden bombsight (12) was rarely carried since horizontal bombing of maneuvering ships at sea proved to be impractical.

Radio Antenna

TBF/TBM-1

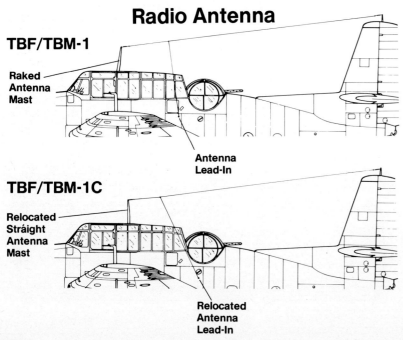

Raked Antenna Mast

Antenna Lead-In

TBF/TBM-1C

Relocated Stráight Antenna Mast

Relocated Antenna Lead-In

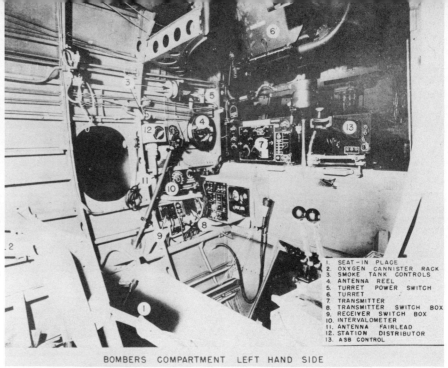

1. SEAT—IN PLACE
2. OXYGEN CANNISTER RACK
3. SMOKE TANK CONTROLS
4. ANTENNA REEL
5. TURRET POWER SWITCH
6. TURRET
7. TRANSMITTER
8. TRANSMITTER SWITCH BOX
9. RECEIVER SWITCH BOX
10. INTERVALOMETER
11. ANTENNA FAIRLEAD
12. STATION DISTRIBUTOR
13. ASB CONTROL

BOMBERS COMPARTMENT LEFT HAND SIDE

The port side of the radioman's station of the TBF. The intervalometer (10) controlled the spacing of bombs being released by the pilot. The radioman would set the desired spacing and the intervalometer actually released the bombs.

The rear of the radioman's station of the TBF-1C. The twin tubes at the rear of the compartment are chutes for launching parachute flares.

1. SPARE AMMUNITION CONTAINER
2. STARTER HANDCRANK- STOWED
3. PARACHUTE RACK
4. FLOAT LIGHTS RACK
5. PARACHUTE FLARE CONTAINERS
6. GUN CAMERA SWITCH BOX
7. SPARE COIL CONTAINERS
8. HEATER TUBE

8992

A TBM-1C of Composite Squadron Seventy-Six (VC-76) taxis clear of the arresting gear aboard USS PETROF BAY (CVE-80) on 30 January 1945. The .50 caliber wing gun blast tubes were usually sealed over with tape to keep out moisture, when the guns were fired the tape was torn away. (USN via David Lucabaugh)

A TBM-1C of VC-17 flown by LT D.J. O'Donovan from NAS Brown Field, California on 12 March 1945. VC-71 was attached to USS MANILA BAY (CVE-61) and carried a White cowling band and White 'U' as squadron identification markings. (USN via Roger Seybel)

USS INTREPID's Air Group Eighteen deployed to Peleliu Island on 24 October 1944. The White 'plus' on the tail of the two VT-18 TBM-1Cs is the geometric identification symbol assigned to INTREPID. One or more of the VF-18 Hellcats parked ahead of the TBMs were flown by the Navy's second ranking ace — LT Cecil E. Harris (24 kills). (USN via David Lucabaugh)

This flak damaged TBM-1C of VT-20 made a safe recovery aboard USS ENTERPRISE (CV-6) on 25 October 1944. The small box mounted in front of the windscreen is a 35 мм gunsight aiming point camera (GSAP) which was activated by the gun trigger and filmed whatever the pilot fired at. (USN via David Lucabaugh)

TBM-1Cs of VT-7 form up for the return flight after striking Japanese targets during a raid on Iwo Jima on 5 November 1944. The Avengers all carry the White 'horseshoe' of USS HANCOCK (CV-19). (NAH-001473)

FLIGHT QUARTERS — a VT-19 pilot carrying his chart board runs to man his TBM-1C aboard USS LEXINGTON (CV-12) on 12 October 1944. The White inverted outline triangle was the identification marking carried by LEXINGTON aircraft. (USN via David Lucabaugh)

Loaded with 5 inch aircraft rockets mounted on Mk 4 rocket rails a TBF-1C of VT-2 patrols above the Saipan invasion fleet during June of 1944. A gun camera is mounted in the ventral machine gun position and could be used to record the results of rocket attacks against Japanese submarines. (USN via Jim Sullivan)

A very weathered, war-weary Avenger on patrol over the Pacific from USS TICONDEROGA (CV-14) on 30 June 1944. This TBM-1C of VT-80 carries four Mk 4 rocket rails, ASB radar antennas on the outer wing panels, and a gun camera mounted just in front of the windscreen. (USN via Jim Sullivan)

An Avenger dives through a sky full of flak bursts as it begins its attack against the Japanese carrier ZUIKAKU (last survivor of the Pearl Harbor raiding force) during the Battle of Leyte Gulf on 15 November 1944. The ZUIKAKU and three other Japanese carriers were sunk during the battle. (Grumman)

Anti-submarine Avengers

The threat posed by the German submarine fleet operating in the Atlantic led to the development of specialized variants of the Avenger and unique anti-submarine forces within the US Navy Allied losses to U-boats were staggering, during February of 1943 alone U-boats sank over 600,000 tons of Allied shipping loaded with supplies vital to the Allied build up in Eurpoe. As Allied land-based patrol aircraft began taking a toll of U-boats, Admiral Donitz moved his U-Boat packs to an area known as the Mid-Atlantic Gap, where they were beyond the range of land-based aircraft.

The US Navy realized that to close the Mid-Atlantic Gap to U-boats an entirely new class of aircraft carrier was needed — the Escort Carrier(CVE). Smaller and slower than the large fleet carriers, CVEs carried twenty to twenty-eight aircraft organized into VCs (Composite Squadrons). The normal aircraft complement for a VC squadron was a mixture of Avengers and Wildcat fighters. With its long range and bomb load of four 350 pound depth charges, the Avenger proved to be highly effective in the anti-submarine role.

In February of 1943, at the peak of the U-boat slaughter, USS BOGUE (CVE-9) and her destroyer escorts began operations in the Atlantic convoy lanes. While the presence of carrier based aircraft prevented many attacks on the ships they escorted, the task force, forced to remain with the convoy, was unable to stay with a sub contact long enough to score a kill. To improve the chances of scoring kills, the Navy changed its tactics and ordered BOGUE and her destroyers to operate offensively as an independent 'Hunter Killer Group'. Freed from the slow speed and restrictive movement of convoy escort duty, the Hunter Killer Group could stay with a sub contact until they scored a kill. Within a week the new tactics were proven when the group sank U-569 and seriously damaged U-231 and U-305.

BOGUE was soon followed by USS BLOCK ISLAND, CORE, GUADALCANAL and ten other CVE Hunter Killer Groups. CVEs proved so effective that between May and December of 1943, only one ship was sunk out of over 2,000 ships sailing in convoys protected by CVEs. Quite a reversal from February when 600,000 tons of shipping were lost.

During 1943 attempts were made to install ASD-1 radar in the Avenger. To mount the ASD radar on the Avenger it was necessary to install the parabolic dish antenna in a radome mounted on the leading edge of the starboard wing. The ASD was a superior radar and was able to detect both surface and airborne targets at a far greater range than the earlier ASB radars. The radome did induce a marked tendency for the starboard wing to stall but since carrier approaches and landings were made 'power on' and well above stall speed this tendency did not present a real problem in service use. TBFs with the ASD radar modification were designated TBF-1Ds and TBMs were designated TBM-1Ds. In addition to the radome mounted ASD-1, a number of TMF/TBM-1D's carried additional yagi radar antennas mounted above each wing just outboard the landing gear well.

USS BOGUE, with VC-19 aboard, had pioneered night anti-submarine operations by modifying two TBF-1Ds to U-boat 'hunters' by removing the turret, wing guns and all armor. Extra fuel tanks were installed in the fuselage and a bomb bay fuel tank was carried, greatly increasing the Avengers range and endurance. With only the pilot and radar operator aboard, these 'Night Owl' Avengers could take off at dusk and remain airborne all night — but they were without offensive armament. If a submarine contact was made these 'hunters' could guide a destroyer to the contact and direct its attack.

One of the most colorful Hunter Killer Group Commanders was Captain Dan Gallery, the Commanding Officer of USS GUADALCANAL (CVE-60). CAPT Gallery originated the concept of standing night patrols with fully armed Avengers. The plan called for operating relays of Avengers throughout the night and making night landings

An Avenger makes a message drop over the crowded deck of an Atlantic CVE. The message drop was a common method of passing information when radio silence was being enforced. The flight deck crew maintains a 'heads-up' attitude both to retrieve the message and to avoid being hit by the weighted message bag. (Grumman)

The Atlantic could be a dangerous place for the small escort carriers, especially in heavy weather. The Avenger is tied down to the flight deck to prevent it from rolling over the side. In heavy seas a number of aircraft were lost when their moorings broke loose. (Grumman)

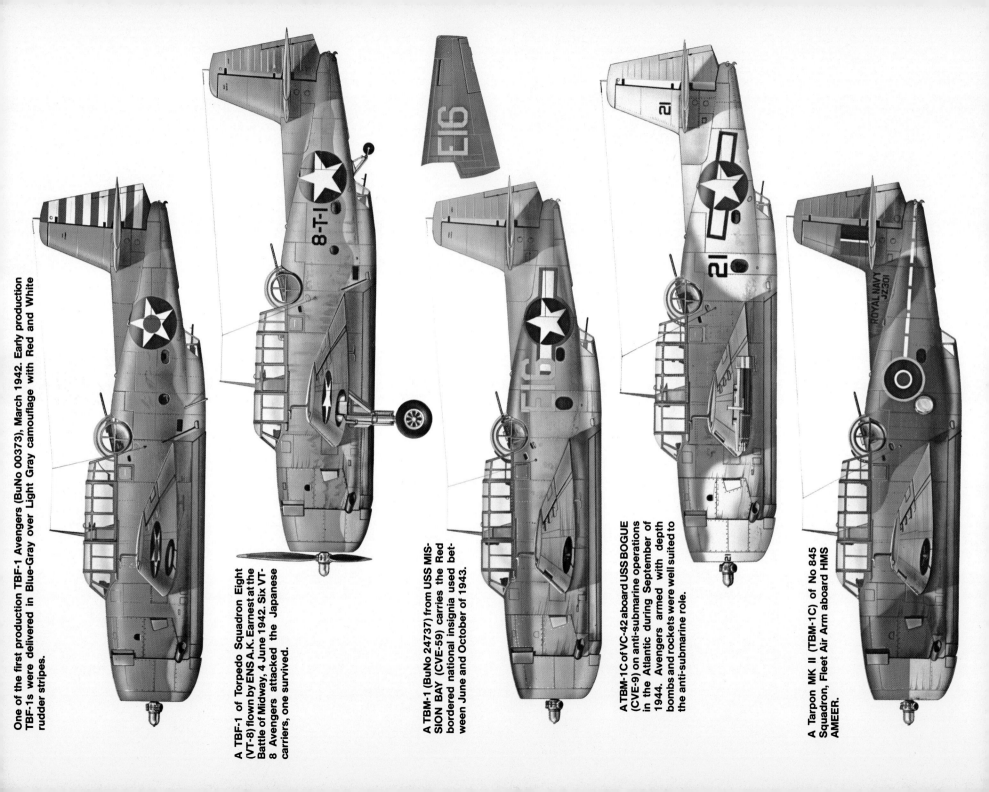

One of the first production TBF-1 Avengers (BuNo 00373), March 1942. Early production TBF-1s were delivered in Blue-Gray over Light Gray camouflage with Red and White rudder stripes.

A TBF-1 of Torpedo Squadron Eight (VT-8) flown by ENS A.K. Earnest at the Battle of Midway, 4 June 1942. Six VT-8 Avengers attacked the Japanese carriers, one survived.

A TBM-1 (BuNo 24737) from USS MIS-SION BAY (CVE-59) carries the Red bordered national insignia used between June and October of 1943.

A TBM-1C of VC-42 aboard USS BOGUE (CVE-9) on anti-submarine operations in the Atlantic during September of 1944. Avengers armed with depth bombs and rockets were well suited to the anti-submarine role.

A Tarpon MK II (TBM-1C) of No 845 Squadron, Fleet Air Arm aboard HMS AMEER.

An overall Sea Blue TBM-3 of VC-9 aboard USS NATOMA BAY (CVE-62) on 7 June 1945.

A TBM-3 of VT-88 carries the White 'RR' identification code assigned to USS YORKTOWN (CV-10) on 27 July 1945.

A Marine TBM-3E of VMTB-132 off of USS CAPE GLOUCESTER during July of 1945. During 1945 several Escort Carriers (CVEs) were assigned to the Marine Corps and carried air groups made up of Marine Corps squadrons.

A TBM-3S of No 825 Squadron, Royal Canadian Navy aboard HMCS MAGNIFICENT. Upper surfaces are Dark Gray over Light Gray.

ble 'diamonds' are the markings carried on all SARGENT BAY aircraft.

and launches. Night carrier operations were still in their infancy and when VC-58 embarked in GUADALCANAL during early 1944, CAPT Gallery presented his plan to the squadron. VC-58's pilots thought the plan feasible and were willing to try. Night flight operations were begun with the aid of a full moon and continued as the moon waned — until the squadron was operating on the darkest of nights — keeping four Avengers airborne all night. For night operations the Avengers were fitted with flame dampening exhausts. The new concept paid handsome dividends, within one 48 hour period of night operations the squadron sank U-68 and U-515.

The primary weapons employed by the Avenger against the German U-Boats were the 350 pound depth charge and a new weapon — aircraft rockets. Rockets were introduced to the US Navy by the British and began reaching the fleet during late 1943. The first Avengers to carry rockets were late production TBF/TBM-1Cs which were modified to carry 3.5 inch Aircraft Rockets mounted on 70 inch British-type rails (designated Mark 4 rocket rails) under the outer wing panels. These Avengers were also modified with a wing rack for drop tanks, depth charges, or small bombs mounted on the wing center section behind the landing gear wheel well. The Mark 4 rail launchers and wing bomb rack reduced the Avengers speed by 17 knots — an acceptable loss to an aircraft operating on anti-submarine operations, but unacceptable for aircraft engaged in attacking heavily armed surface ships or land targets.

To reduce the drag of the Mk 4 rail, the California Institute of Technology developed an improved rocket launching system, the Mark 5 zero length launcher. Launcher drag and weight were significantly reduced and as long as the rockets were fired at air speeds of 200 knots (230 mph) or more the rockets would follow as accurate a trajectory as those launched from the earlier Mark 4 rails. To increase firepower five inch warheads were mounted on 3.5 inch rocket motors under the designation 5 inch Aircraft Rocket (AR).

An improved rocket, the 5 inch HVAR (High Velocity Aircraft Rocket), called the 'Holy Moses', was developed by Cal Tech with a 5 inch case-hardened steel warhead attached to a 5 inch rocket motor. These rockets now gave an Avenger the firepower of a destroyer when the eight rockets were fired in salvo. The first combat use of rockets by a US aircraft took place on 11 January 1944, when two rocket armed TBF-1Cs of VC-58, flown by LTJGs L.L. McFord and W.D. Seeley, caught a German U-boat (U-758) on the surface. The Avengers scored two probable and two certain rocket hits on the U-boat then followed up with a depth bomb attack. In the Pacific theater aircraft rockets first went into combat on 31 January 1944 when Avengers of VC-7 aboard USS MANILA BAY (CVE-61) attacked ammunition and fuel dumps on Bigej Island in the Marshall's chain.

By 1945, the Hunter-Killer Groups had virtually eliminated the U-boat threat in the Atlantic and it had became increasingly difficult for them to locate targets. For the loss of one CVE (BLOCK ISLAND was torpedoed by U-549 with USS ELMORE sinking U-549 later the same day), the fourteen Atlantic CVE groups sank a total of fifty-three U-boats and captured U-505. The USS BOGUE hunter-killer group was the Atlantic high scorer with twelve confirmed kills.

The Avenger/CVE team also operated in the anti-submarine role in the Pacific Theater and were credited with eleven Japanese submarines. USS ANZIO (CVE-57) was the Pacific champ with five confirmed kills.

An Avenger of the Naval Experimental Station, Philidelpha, Pennsylvania carries an experimental ASD-1 radar installation on the canopy. This installation proved impractical and the radome was moved back to the leading edge of the starboard wing on the TBF/TBM-1D. (USN via Jim Sullivan)

TBF/TBM-1D ASD Radome (Starboard Wing)

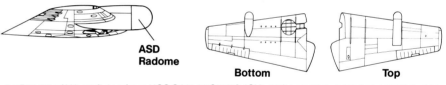

ASD Radome   Bottom   Top

A TBM-1D of VT-51 flying from USS SAN JACINTO (CVL-30) on anti-submarine patrol during July of 1944. The TBM-1D carried ASD-1 radar in a streamlined radome mounted on the starboard wing leading edge. The ASD-1 range varied considerably, the author was able to get an 80 mile range, and large land masses could be picked up at distances up to 100 miles. (USN via David Lucabaugh)

A TBM-1C of VT-10 flying from USS YORKTOWN (CV-10) carries four 70 inch British style Mk 4 rocket rails under each wing. The small 'T' shaped antenna under the inner port wing is a radio altimeter antenna. (USN via David Lucabaugh)

A TBF-1C unfolds its wings while waiting to take off from USS GUADALCANAL (CVE-60) during April of 1944. Anti-submarine Avengers were normally armed with Mk 54 depth bombs and rockets. The drag of the early Mk 4 rocket rails reduced the Avengers airspeed by 17 knots. (NAH-00173)

A TBF-1C of VC-58 makes a low pass over the captured German submarine U-505. The German crew had opened the sea cocks to scuttle the sub, but boarding parties from USS PILLSBURY and USS GUADALCANAL entered the conning tower hatch and successfully closed the sea cocks. U505 was the only German submarine captured by US forces on the high seas. And is now on display at the Museum of Science and Industry in Chicago. (Grumman)

MK-4 70 inch Rocket Rails (TBF/TBM-1C)

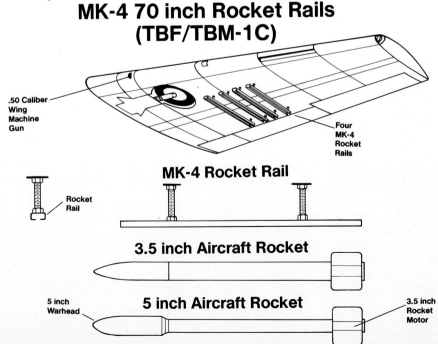

.50 Caliber Wing Machine Gun

Four MK-4 Rocket Rails

MK-4 Rocket Rail

Rocket Rail

3.5 inch Aircraft Rocket

5 inch Aircraft Rocket

5 inch Warhead

3.5 inch Rocket Motor

On 18 September 1944, this VC-42 TBM-1C has gone over the barrier on USS BOGUE (CVE-9) and crashed into other Avengers parked forward on the flight deck. For destroying three TBMs, the pilot was awarded a mock Iron Cross by his squadron mates. (USN via David Lucabaugh)

During flight operations on 4 November 1944 a TMB-3 of VC-55 stalled out on landing and went over the side of USS CROATAN (CVE-25). A gun camera has been installed outboard of the Mk 5 rocket launchers on the port wing. Yagi ASB radar antennas are mounted on top of each wing. (USN via David Lucabaugh)

This TBM-1 was one of six USS MISSION BAY (CVE-59) Avengers modified to carry the Cal-Tech retro-bomb and Magnetic Anomaly Detector (MAD) equipment (mounted in the 'stinger' position). The retro-bomb had a small rocket motor which stopped the bomb's forward movement and allowed it to drop vertically. (USN via David Lucabaugh)

MK-5 Zero Length Rocket Launchers

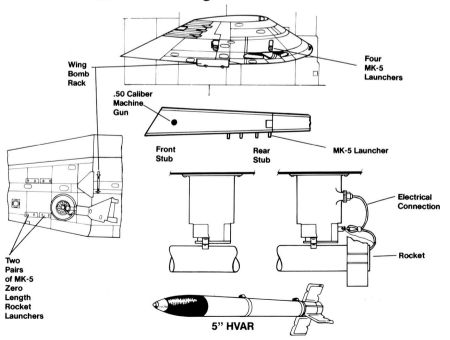

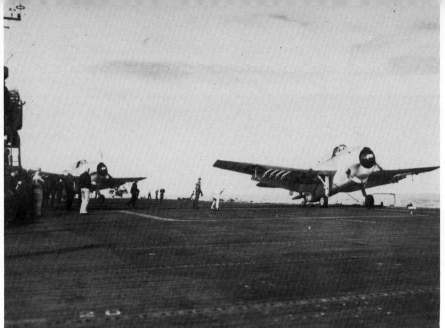

Two TBM-1Cs armed with 3.5 inch aircraft rockets on Mk 4 rails are prepared for catapult launch from an Atlantic based CVE. The Avengers are painted in the ASW II camouflage scheme of Dark Gull Gray and Insignia White. (USN via MAJ J.M. Elliott, USMC-Ret.)

A TMB-1C of an Atlantic CVE is equipped with flame damping exhausts for night operations. The propeller hub and a portion of each propeller blade were painted in Non-Specular Insignia White in keeping with the aircraft camouflage. (Grumman)

ARM3/c Charles Gertsch, LTJG L.L. McFord and AMM2/c W.H. Ryder of VC-58 are credited with the first American rocket attack against an enemy submarine on 11 January 1944. The name *Len Sharon* in Black on the nose is unusual for a carrier based aircraft since Navy policy discouraged personal markings.(Grumman)

Exhaust Flame Dampers

Standard TBF/TBF Exhaust

Night Flame Dampening Exhaust

TBM-3

During February of 1943 the Navy requested Grumman to investigate ways to increase the power of the Avenger. In response Grumman undertook a design study of an improved Avenger with a 2,000 hp Pratt and Whitney R-2800 engine and a Martin 250CE turret. The high demand for the Pratt and Whitney engine for other higher priority aircraft prevented the design study from progressing but the need for additional engine power for the Avenger was now recognized.

Wright was also engaged in a program to increase the horsepower of their R-2600-8 engine and had developed the 1,900 hp XR-2600-10. The engine was the same size and weight as the R-2600-8 but offered an additional 200 horsepower. Grumman had retained two Avenger airframes at Bethpage for test use and these were modified to accept the new engine. One airframe was fitted with the 1,900 hp XR-2600-10 engine under the designation XTBF-2 while the second airframe was fitted with a still further improved 1,900 hp Wright R-2600-20 engine becoming the XTBF-3.

After a short test program, the R-2600-20 powered XTBF-3 was selected for further development. The new engine required a redesign of the cowling to provide adequate cooling and airflow for engine's repositioned oil cooler with the oil cooler air intake being moved to the bottom lip of the cowling. To further improve cooling, four additional cowl flaps were installed on each side of the cowling. The two bottom cowl flap on each side were indented and the lowest flap on each side was notched to clear the exhaust stack.

The TBM-3 retained the gun armed wings of the TBF-1C with Mk 5 zero-length rocket launchers standardized in place of the earlier Mk 4 rocket rails. The cockpit instruments were re-arranged and to improve the pilots night vision the instrument panel lighting was changed from direct ultra violet lighting to indirect red lighting. A number of TBM-3s, like the earlier TBF/TBM-1Cs were fitted with an AN/APS-3 radar mounted in a radome attached to the leading edge of the starboard wing under the designation TBM-3D.

Grumman delivered two XTBF-3s prototypes to the Navy in October of 1943. After acceptance tests the Navy officially accepted the design and assigned production to Eastern Aircraft under the designation TBM-3. The TBM-3 would become the main Avenger production variant with over 4,000 being produced before the end of the war.

The Grumman XTBF-3 prototype parked on the grass at Bethpage during October of 1943. The TBM-3 featured a reconfigured cowling for the 1,900 hp Wright R-2800-20 engine, with four cowl flaps on each side and an oil cooler intake added to the lower cowl lip. (Grumman)

Cowling

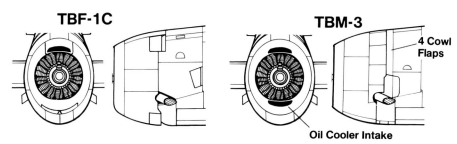

TBF-1C

TBM-3

4 Cowl Flaps

Oil Cooler Intake

(Right) The pilot of a TBM-3 of VC-93 braces himself for a catapult launch from USS MAKIN ISLAND (CVE-93) on 4 March 1945. The four cowling flaps are open to provide engine cooling as the Avenger is brought to full power for takeoff. (USN via David Lucabaugh)

A TBM-3 receives the launch signal from the flight deck officer and begins its takeoff roll from USS FRANKLIN (CV-13) during March of 1944. The Avenger is fitted with ASB radar antennas and Mk 5 rocket launchers on the outer wing panels. (USN via David Lucabaugh)

A pair of TBM-3s of VC-72 from USS TULAGI (CVE-72) during March of 1945 carry 5 inch aircraft rockets on Mk 5 launchers. The crewman, behind the pilot in the lead Avenger, is holding a K-20 aerial still camera. (USN via David Lucabaugh)

A TBM-3 painted in the Atlantic Anti-submarine II camouflage paint scheme of Dark Gull Grey and Insignia White carries a camera mounted under the port wing to record rocket attacks against German U-boats. (T.C. Tillar via Jim Sullivan)

F6F-5 Hellcats escort a TBM-3 of VT-40 on a mission from USS SUWANNEE (CVE-27). The name *DoT.* just below and forward of the cockpit and the aircraft side number on the extreme rear fuselage below the tailplane are unusual. Few Navy aircraft carried personal markings. (USN via Jim Sullivan)

This TBM-3D carries 5 inch HVAR rockets, an ASD radar in the radome mounted on the starboard wing leading edge, a search light mounted under the port wing, and ASB radar yagi antennas on top of the wings. (USN via MAJ John Elliott, USMC)

A flight of TBM-3s of VT-4 returning to USS ESSEX (CV-9) after a strike against Japanese installations around Saigon on 12 January 1945. Both Avengers in the foreground have faint remnants of an earlier Temporary White ferry number (404 and 24) on the fuselage just ahead of the wing root. (USN via Jim Sullivan)

A TBM-3 of VT-84 on its final approach to USS BUNKER HILL (CV-17) on 5 April 1945. The Avenger's retractable tail hook is down and ready to catch an arresting wire on the carrier's deck. The White arrow on the fin is the identification marking carried by BUNKER HILL aircraft. (USN via David Lucabaugh)

Avengers of VC-88 from USS SAGINAW BAY (CVE-82) enroute to targets during March of 1945. The lead Avenger carries VC-88's 'twin lightning bolts' markings in White on a Glossy Sea Blue tail, while the wingman's Avenger carries the markings on a Intermediate Blue tail. (USN via David Lucabaugh)

33

Flight deck emergency personnel carrying fire extinguishers move in on a TBM-3 of VC-83 after it went into the barrier aboard USS SARGENT BAY (CVE-83) on 14 June 1945. (USN via David Lucabaugh)

The deck crew aboard USS ENTERPRISE (CV-6) disengages the tail hook of a TBM-3 of VT(N)-90 on 8 March 1945. The machine guns have been removed from the turret, and 'stinger' position. During this period ENTERPRISE was operating as a night carrier and VT(N)-90 was employed on night intruder missions. (USN via David Lucabaugh)

34

The 275 gallon jettisonable bomb bay fuel tank carried in the bomb bay was a Grumman design and gave the Avenger a maximum range of 2180 miles. Normally the fuel in the bomb bay tank would be used first since the tank was not self-sealing. (Grumman)

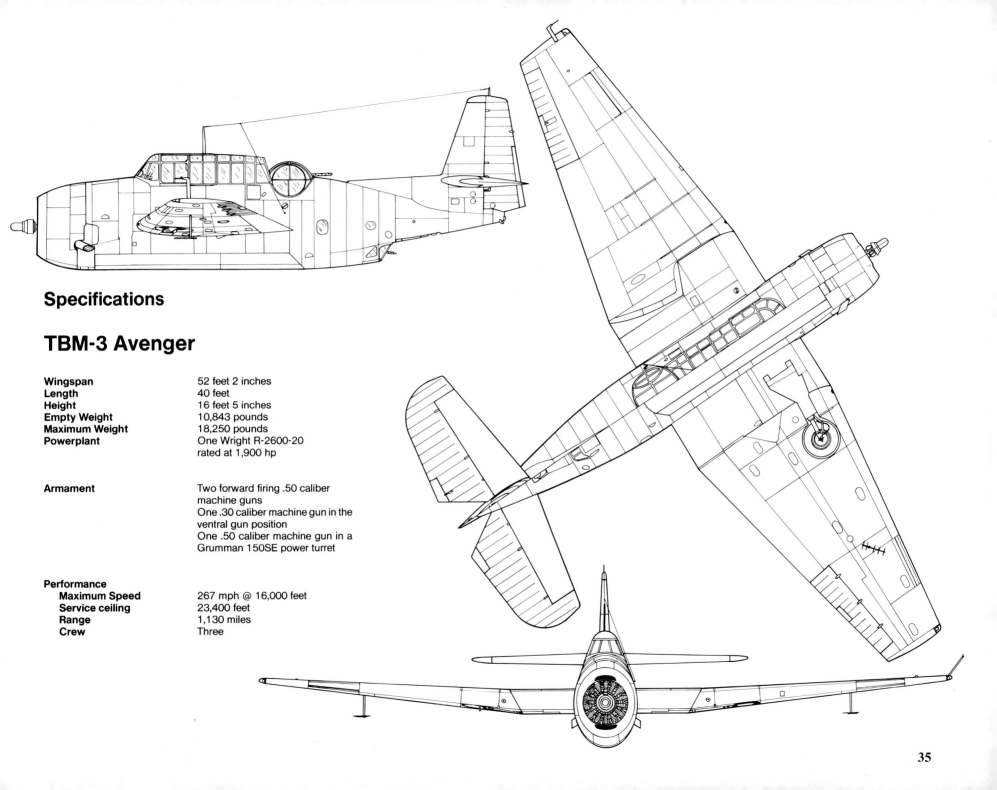

Specifications

TBM-3 Avenger

Wingspan	52 feet 2 inches
Length	40 feet
Height	16 feet 5 inches
Empty Weight	10,843 pounds
Maximum Weight	18,250 pounds
Powerplant	One Wright R-2600-20 rated at 1,900 hp
Armament	Two forward firing .50 caliber machine guns One .30 caliber machine gun in the ventral gun position One .50 caliber machine gun in a Grumman 150SE power turret

Performance

Maximum Speed	267 mph @ 16,000 feet
Service ceiling	23,400 feet
Range	1,130 miles
Crew	Three

A Marine Corps TBM-3 taxis past an abandoned F4U-1 Corsair which has been cannibalized for spare parts on an Pacific island during 1944. The hard rubber tail wheel tire has been replaced by a larger pneumatic tire for operations on land. (USN via Jim Sullivan)

A TBM-3 of VT-45 'traps' (catches an arresting cable) aboard USS SAN JACINTO (CVL-30) on 21 March 1945. The cables running across the deck just behind the parked Avengers are the crash barrier, designed to stop any landing aircraft that failed to engage an arresting cable. (USN via David Lucabaugh)

Flight deck crew folds the wings of a battle damaged TMB-3 of VT-82 aboard USS BENNINGTON (CV-20) on 7 April 1945. SB2C Helldiver squadrons were often withdrawn from Essex class carriers and replaced by F4U Corsair fighter squadrons, but the Avengers remained until V-J Day and beyond. (USN via David Lucabaugh)

TBM-3 of VT-83 taxis forward on USS ESSEX (CV-9) 19 April 1945. The White 'double triangle' is the geometric recognition marking assigned to all ESSEX aircraft. Avengers during WWII have often been mistakenly identified as carrying overall Glossy Sea Blue paint. In fact Avengers carried Glossy Sea Blue on the upper surfaces only, with Non-Specular Sea Blue on the lower fuselage sides and under-surfaces. (USN via David Lucabaugh)

An overall Sea Blue TBM-3 of VC-9 is launched from USS NATOMA BAY (CVE-62) on 7 June 1945 while crewman make repairs to the forward flight deck. The Avenger is a late production TBM-3 and carries an APS-4 radar pod under the starboard wing. (Richard M. Hill)

Carrying the White Shamrock and crossed Irish pipes of USS SHAMROCK BAY (CVE-84) a TBM-3 of VC-94 is prepared for launching on the port catapult. The thirty-five White mission markings under the cockpit are an unusual marking for a carrier based aircraft. (USN via David Lucabaugh)

VT-4's pilots are shown with one of the squadron's TBM-3s aboard ESSEX in December 1944. ENS Bill Cannady is third from left on the wing and ENS Lloyd Cole fourth from left in the front row. (USN via LCDR Wm.H. Cannady)

VT-4's Chief Petty Officers and aircrewman with the same TBM-3 aboard ESSEX. Two 5" HVAR ('Holy Moses') rockets are mounted on Mk 5 launchers under the wing and an ASB Yagi radar antenna is outboard of the rockets. (USN via LCDR Wm.H. Cannady)

(Below) On 27 July 1945 the Navy assigned letter identification codes to all ESSEX and INDEPENDENCE class carriers replacing the earlier geometric symbols. This formation of TBM-3s of VT-88 carry USS YORKTOWN's (CV-10) 'RR' code in White on the tail. (USN via Jim Sullivan)

Tarpon/Avenger Mk I, II, III
Great Britain

To replace the obsolete Fairly Swordfish and Albacore biplane torpedo bombers in use aboard Royal Navy carriers, the British requested that the 1942 Lend-lease program include a number of TBF-1s. Initially early Avengers delivered to the British under Lend-lease were given a special US Navy designation TBF-1B and named Tarpon Mk I by the British. As the program expanded and later models were delivered, the Navy dropped the system of assigning special designations for aircraft supplied to the British.

The Avenger would become one of the most important carrier based aircraft in the Fleet Air Arm and a total of 958 Avengers of all variants would be delivered to the British (402 TBF-1B Tarpon/Avenger Mk I, 334 TBM-1C Tarpon/Avenger Mk II, and 222 TBM-3 Tarpon/Avenger MK III) during the Second World War. The TBFs and TBMs in British service retained the Tarpon designation until January of 1944, when all aircraft were re-named Avenger to avoid confusion when operating with American forces in the Pacific.

After delivery to England, the Avengers were modified to meet specific British requirements by Blackburn Aircraft Ltd. British gun sights, radio equipment and oxygen systems were installed replacing American systems. The cockpit was modified to position the navigator immediately behind the pilot, attachment points were installed for rocket assisted take-off equipment, a camera mount for an F-24 aerial camera was fitted in the radioman's station, the radio aerial mast was hinged so that it could be folded over to clear the lower overhead of British carrier hangar bays. To improve visibility from the radioman's station the two oval windows on the fuselage sides were replaced by bulged dome shaped windows.

The first British squadron to operationally deploy with Tarpon Mk Is was Number 832 Squadron. Initially formed at Naval Air Station, Norfolk, Virginia, Number 832 Squadron, with fifteen Tarpon Mk Is, sailed with HMS VICTORIOUS and USS SARATOGA for operations in the Solomon Islands during the Summer of 1943. Later HMS VICTORIOUS took part in the invasion of New Georgia before returning to England.

In Europe, Fleet Air Arm Avengers were primarily used in the North Atlantic and North Sea areas for both anti-submarine operations, and attacks against German shipping off the Norwegian coast. A number of British Avenger squadrons were land based, flying anti-submarine, mine laying, and anti-shipping patrols over the English Channel. During the summer of 1944 at the height of the German V-1 'buzz' bomb attacks, Avengers of Number 854 and Number 855 Squadrons were credited with destruction of two V-1s, both shot down by gunfire.

In 1945 the Royal Navy selected the Avenger as the principal naval strike aircraft for squadrons being sent to the Pacific. Cooperation between the British and American Fleets was being accelerated for the final assault against Japan in which British Avenger squadrons would play a significant role. No.s 820, 849, 854 and 857 Squadrons were deployed with a total of eight-four Avenger Mk IIIs (TBM-3s) aboard four British carriers; HMS ILLUSTRIOUS, INDEFATIGABLE, INDOMITABLE and VICTORIOUS as part of the British Pacific Fleet. The British Pacific Fleet joined with American units becoming Task Force 57 under the tactical control of the US Navy's Fifth Fleet.

A Royal Navy Tarpon Mk I (TBF-1B) on its acceptance flight over Long Island Sound during 1943. Fleet Air Arm Tarpon Is were delivered in British camouflage of Dark Slate Grey, Extra Dark Sea Grey over Sky Type S. (Grumman)

On 24 January 1945, Task Force 57 began a series of attacks against the oil refineries at Palembang, on the island of Sumatra (Dutch East Indies). The British attacks almost totally destroyed the refineries adding to the already critical shortage of fuel for the Japanese war machine. Royal Navy Avenger squadrons flew a total of ninety-five sorties against Sumatra losing six Avengers.

Task Force 57 also took part in the Okinawa campaign, where British Avenger squadrons were assigned the destruction of Japanese airfields on Formosa in an effort to lessen the numbers of *Kamikaze* aircraft available to the Japanese for attacks on the Allied Fleet off Okinawa. During July of 1945 the British Pacific Fleet was re-numbered Task Force 37, taking part in air strikes against the Japanese Home Islands. On 24 July, an Avenger of Number 848 Squadron became the first British aircraft to bomb Japan.

When the war ended the Fleet Air Arm rapidly phased out the Avenger and large numbers of Avengers were jettisoned at sea. The last British wartime Avenger squadron was officially disbanded in June of 1946.

Radioman's Windows

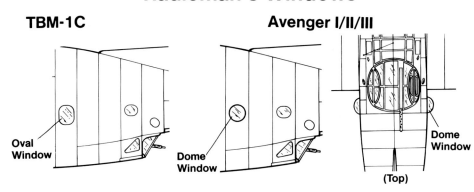

TBM-1C

Oval Window

Avenger I/II/III

Dome Window

Dome Window

(Top)

British ordnancemen clean an American .50 caliber Browning machine gun during training. The head of the bending crewman partially obscures the bulged dome observers window which was fitted to all British Avengers. The antenna mast was hinged to fold over because of the lower hangar deck clearance of British aircraft carriers. (Grumman)

Two Fleet Air Arm Tarpon Mk IIs (TBF-1Cs) share the Grumman ramp with dozens of new US Navy F6F-3 Hellcats awaiting delivery during late 1943. The British would receive a total of 958 Avengers before the war ended. (Grumman)

British aircrews in operational training at a US Naval Air Station are wearing a mix of British and American flight gear. The aircrewman in the center is wearing a US Navy flight helmet and goggles with a distinctively British style ascot. (Grumman)

Six Fleet Air Arm Tarpon Mk IIs on patrol over the Atlantic. The bulged dome windows on the fuselage sides were the Tarpon's distinctive external feature. (Grumman)

Tarpon II (TBF-1C) of No. 845 Squadron is catapulted from HMS AMEER during operations in 1944. The cable under the Avenger is the catapult tow bridle. (National Museums of Canada)

TARPON Is warm-up their engines at a British air base. Land based Avengers flew anti-submarine patrols, mining operations and anti-shipping sweeps over the English Channel and North Sea. The squadron codes on the fuselage side are Red with a thin White outline. (Grumman)

TBM-3E

In an effort to again improve the performance of the TBM-3, Eastern began a program to both lighten and strengthen the standard Avenger's airframe. This new light weight variant weighed nearly a ton less than a standard TBM-3 and was approved for production under the designation TBM-3E during late 1944.

The engine cowl flaps on the TBM-3E were further refined and of equal size without indentation although the bottom flaps were notched to clear the exhaust pipe. The retractable tail hook was replaced by a non-retractable unit located on an external mounting just under the tail (the external tail hook extended beyond the rudder and added a foot to the length of the TBM-3E), and the 'stinger' gun position was deleted. An underwing rack for an AN/APS-4 radar pod was installed under the starboard wing outboard of the Mk 5 rocket launchers. The lighter weight of the TBM-3E increased maximum speed to 276 mph at 16,500 feet and improved its rate of climb to 2,060 feet per minute.

LCDR Bill Cannady, who flew TBM-3Es with VT-4 aboard USS ESSEX during 1945, reported that the turret gunner's escape hatch on the TBM-3Es were notorious for coming loose and flying off the aircraft during high-G pull-outs. One such incident happened to the aircraft he was flying and the hatch struck the port stabilizer, cutting off part of the stabilizer and elevator. He was able to return and land aboard ESSEX where he was reprimanded for not having declared an emergency. The problem was finally corrected by squadron maintenance personnel who devised an improved weather stripping for the escape hatch. The stripping improved the hatch's seal against the airstream which prevented the metal fatigue that caused the hatch locking pins to fail.

When Japan surrendered in August of 1945, the Navy cancelled all Avenger contracts. Avenger production terminated during September of 1945 when the last twenty-four TBM-3Es were delivered to the Navy. The Avenger, however, would continue in service for many years to come. The large internal volume of the Avengers bomb bay and fuselage made it an ideal platform for carrying a increasing amount and variety of electronics. The TBM-3/3E airframe would serve as the basis for a number of specialized variants that would serve the US Navy until June of 1954 when the last Avenger was retired from active service.

TBM-3N — specially equipped for night attack.
TBM-3U — utility and target towing variant with all weapons and armor removed.
TBM-3Q — radar countermeasures aircraft, equipped with electronic jamming equipment in a radome similar to the TBM-3W.
TBM-3P — photo reconnaissance variant with aerial cameras mounted in the bomb bay.
TBM-3L — modified with a search light carried on a retractable mount in the bomb bay.
TBM-3H — modified with a surface search radar.
TBM-3M — service conversions with missile launching equipment for various post war missile test programs.

Exported widely, the Avenger also served with at least seven foreign navies and air forces (Great Britian, New Zealand, Netherlands, Canada, France, Japan, and Uruguay) into the 1960s.

A TBM-3E of VT-86 prepares for takeoff from USS WASP (CV-18) during October of 1945. The radioman's 'stinger' gun postion was deleted on the light weight TBM-3E and the earlier retractable tail hook was replaced by an externally mounted non-retractable hook. (USN via David Lucabaugh)

Tail Hook

TBM-3

Fully Retractable Tail Hook

TBM-3E

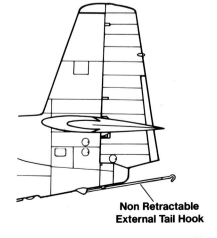

Non Retractable External Tail Hook

A flight of TBM-3Es of VT-34 return to USS MONTEREY (CVL-26) on 29 Aug 1945. The demarcation line between the upper surfaces of Glossy Sea Blue and Non-Specular Sea Blue lower surfaces is easily seen. Markings such as the White mission marks just below the cockpit and the shapely pin up girl on the fuselage are extremely rare on a Navy aircraft. The white pod under the starboard wing is an AN/APS-4 radar pod. (USN via Nick Waters)

A flight of TMB-3Es of Marine Torpedo Squadron 132 (VMTB-132) from USS CAPE GLOUCHES-TER (CVE-109) off the Chinese coast on 29 July 1945. During 1945 several CVEs carried air groups made up entirely of Marine squadrons. (USN via Jim Sullivan)

This early prooduction TBM-3E of VMTB-234 from USS VELA GULF (CVE-111) still has the retractable tailhook. The ASP-4 surface search radar pod was found to be more practical than the earlier fixed radomes mounted on the wing of the TBM-3D and became a standard feature on TBM-3Es. (USN via David Lucabaugh)

Cowling

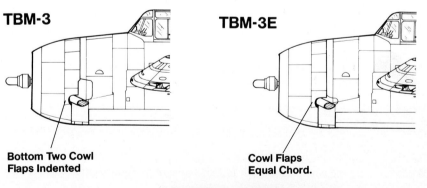

TBM-3

Bottom Two Cowl Flaps Indented

TBM-3E

Cowl Flaps Equal Chord.

AN/APS-4 Radar Pod

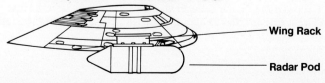

Wing Rack

Radar Pod

A TBM-3E unfolds its wings as it is directed forward into takeoff position from USS PHILIPPINE SEA (CV-47) during 1948. A carrier's flight deck full of whirling propellers is an extremely dangerous place, unforgiving of the slightest mistake. (USN via George Haddad)

Ventral Gun Position

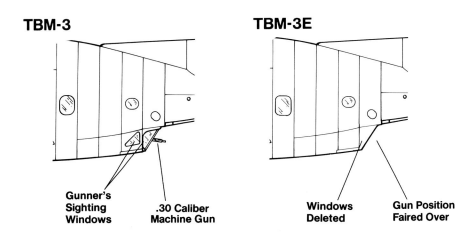

TBM-3

Gunner's Sighting Windows
.30 Caliber Machine Gun

TBM-3E

Windows Deleted
Gun Position Faired Over

A pair of TBM-3Es during a postwar anti-submarine training excercise. The Trailing Radio Antenna under the port wing was used for aircraft to ship radio communications with the destroyer, USS GURKE (DD 783), and would (hopefully) be reeled-in before landing. (Grumman)

After the war Avengers were transfered to the Naval Reserve and equipped a number of reserve squadrons. This TBM-3E was flown by LT Bob Hassler of VS-833, a Reserve squadron based at Naval Air Station Floyd Bennett Field, New York on 17 October 1954.(USN via Roger Seybel)

43

TBM-3R

Shortly after the start of the Korean War, the Navy realized it needed a cargo aircraft with the capability of delivering vital supplies to aircraft carriers at sea. A special Navy air transport group was formed with modified Avengers and assigned to Fleet Aircraft Service Squadron Eleven (FASRON-11) in Japan. The new unit immediately began operations ferrying men and supplies to the carriers in combat off the Korean coast.

The Avenger, with its range, endurance, and internal load carrying capability offered the ideal solution to creating a carrier based cargo aircraft. Existing TBM-3 and TBM-3E airframes were converted to transport variants under the designation TBM-3R and the Carrier On Board Delivery (COD) aircraft was born. The transport conversion consisted of removing the turret, bombing systems, guns and armor. The canopy was reconfigured to enclose the turret opening and seats for seven passengers were installed in the cockpit and radioman's station. The bomb bay was modified to accept stretchers for casualty evacuation missions. A number of different canopy configurations were installed, some Avengers had a metal faring covering the turret opening and a large split window installed which served as an entry hatch for passengers. Other canopy configurations were all glass with a plexiglas faring enclosing the turret opening.

To speed delivery of bulky cargo to carriers operating off Korea, a unique method of carrying the cargo was designed by a FasRon-11 Chief Petty Officer. He designed a wire screen basket that was tailored to fit the bomb bay of the TBM-3R. Bomb hoists were used to raise and lower the loaded cargo basket from the Avengers bomb bay. A loaded basket could be removed and another quickly substituted, allowing for a fast turnaround at either end of the trip. Mail, vital aircraft parts, electronics equipment, and medical supplies were just some of the cargo carried by the COD Avenger. The Carrier On Board Delivery concept was proven to be viable and the success of the TBM-3R led to a new class of carrier aircraft in Fleet Logistics Squadrons. Today the COD function is carried out by another Grumman aircraft, the turboprop C-2 Greyhound.

A TBM-3R of the First Marine Air Wing at Pokang Korea during the Spring of 1951. Marine TBM-3Rs were used extensively in the casualty evacuation role, flying seriously wounded men to hospitals in Japan. (Elliot J. Kimble)

A number of TBM-3Es were modified for Carrier On-board Delivery (COD) duties with the turret removed and the opening faired over. Redesignated TBM-3Rs the COD Avengers had provisions for the installation of up to seven seats in the cockpit and radioman's station.

Canopy Variations

Metal

Metal

Bomb Bay Cargo Basket

Aluminum Tubing

Wire Mesh

(Above) A pair of TBM-3Rs of VR-21 go through final engine checks before take off from Itazuke, Japan during 1951. These TMB-3Rs have a glass panel fairing instead of a metal fairing over the turret position. (Grumman)

(Below) A TBM-3R of VR-21 has just delivered its cargo and passengers to K-18, a forward airfield in Korea during 1951. VR-21 used its fleet of TBM-3Rs to ferry men and supplies between the carriers, Japan, and Korea. (Grumman)

45

TBM-3S

The *Cold War* of the 1950s was a period of increasing tensions between East and West. The Soviet Union, realizing that Germany had nearly won the Battle of the Atlantic with its U-boat fleet, began building and deploying the world's largest submarine fleet. The threat of Soviet submarines prompted the US Navy to increase its emphasis on anti-submarine warfare and to develop aircraft specially outfitted to hunt and kill submarines. The Avenger had proven to be well suited for anti-submarine warfare during the Battle of the Atlantic and the Navy again turned to the Avenger to meet the new threat.

A number of existing TBM-3E airframes were modified for the ASW mission with new electronics and weapons. The turret was removed and the opening faired over. The area formerly taken up by the turret became a crew station for a radar operator/navigator. The canopy was modified with metal panels replacing portions of the greenhouse. Provisions were made for mounting a searchlight under the port wing, sonobuoy launch tubes were installed at the rear of the radioman's station. Since the TBM-3S would be flown at low level, the oxygen system was deleted. To receive radar information from a radar search aircraft a data-link system was installed with an antenna being mounted on the top of the rudder. Anti-submarine weapons such as depth bombs and acostic homing torpedos were housed in the bomb bay and the wings retained the Mk 5 zero length rocket launchers of the TBM-3E.

During 1953 a number of Avengers were delivered to the British under the designation Avenger AS4. These aircraft were modified to carry a surface search radar mounted in a radome under the forward fuselage with the electronics carried in the forward portion of the bomb bay. The Avenger AS Mk 4 served with seven Royal Navy squadrons during the 1950's and the last AS Mk 4 (attached to No 831 Electronics Counter-Measures Squadron) was not phased out until the early 1960's. When the Japanese Maritime Self Defense Force was formed on 1 July 1954, Avengers formed the initial equipment for the JMSDF's air arm. Other TBM-3S aircraft were exported under the Military Assistance Program to Canada, France, and the Netherlands. These export ASW Avengers carried a variety of canopy modifications.

A number of TBM-3E airframes were modified for the anti-submarine strike role under the designation TBM-3S. This TBM-3S carries a search light mounted under the port wing and a data link antenna mounted on the top of the rudder. The White rectangle on the center fuselage is the hatch for the life raft stowage compartment. (Grumman)

The TBM-3S normally operated with the TBM-3W radar search aircraft and served as the strike aircraft ('Killer') of an ASW 'Hunter-Killer' team. Operating independently, the 'Hunter-Killer' team could track and attack unfriendly submarines operating in the vicinity of the carrier task group without the assistance of surface units. Lessons learned with the TBM-3S led to an increasingly complex and sophisticated class of carrier based anti-submarine warfare aircraft that has culminated in today's Lockheed S-3A Viking.

Canopy Variations

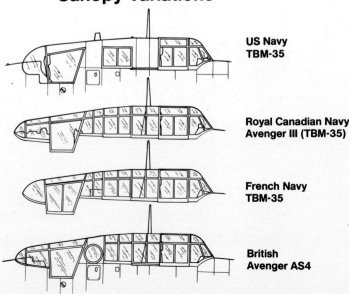

US Navy
TBM-3S

Royal Canadian Navy
Avenger III (TBM-3S)

French Navy
TBM-3S

British
Avenger AS4

(Above) Avengers were exported through the Foreign Military Assistance Program during the late 1940s and early 1950s. A number of TBM-3S anti-submarine Avengers were delivered to the French *Aeronaval*. This overall Glossy Sea Blue Avenger of *Flottille 3S* was based at Cuers in southern France. Avengers served in the French Navy until 1966.

125 Avengers served with three Royal Canadian Navy squadrons from 1950 to 1957. This TBM-3S of No. 825 Squadron passes over the Canadian carrier HMCS MAGNIFICENT during 1951. Canadian Avengers carried a Dark Sea Grey over Light Sea Grey camouflage scheme and a Red and White striped tailhook. (National Museums of Canada)

When the Japanese armed forces were re-established on 1 July 1954, Avengers were part of the initial equipment of the Japanese Maritime Self Defense Force for anti-submarine duties. Japanese Avengers were painted Light Gull Gray over White with Gloss Black numbers and Japanese characters. (Lt.Col Akihiko Korenaga)

Ventral "Dustbin" Radome
(British Avenger AS4)

This restored TBM-3S belongs to the Confederate Air Force (CAF), a Texas based organization devoted to preserving WW II aircraft. The CAF has painted it in the 1943-44 'tri-color' camouflage scheme (which the TBM-3S never carried). The external tail hook mounting is located under the tail but the tail hook has been removed. (Rick Brownlee)

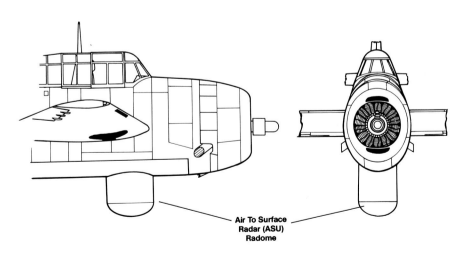

Air To Surface
Radar (ASU)
Radome

TBM-3W

Early in the Second World War the Navy realized that ship board search radars could not detect aircraft flying low over the water soon enough to provide adequate warning of an attack. A radar antenna mounted on a fifty foot mast would not detect aircraft flying at 500 feet or below until the aircraft was within 20 miles of the ship. The solution was obvious, raise the height of the radar antenna by mounting it in an orbiting aircraft.

During early 1942, the Navy funded a series of experiments at the Radiation Laboratory of the Massachusetts Institute of Technology which culminated in the development of the APS-20 radar, a radar light enough to be carried by an aircraft yet powerful enough to detect targets up to 136 miles from the carrier. Assigned the code name of *Project Caddilac*, this airborne radar development project was given top priority. Since the aircraft was to be carrier based and needed sufficient internal space to mount the radar's electronics, the project engineers selected the TBM-3 Avenger as the aircraft best suited for conversion.

A TBM-3 airframe was extensively modified to carry the radar under the designation TBM-3W. All armor, guns, and bombing systems were removed. The radar was installed in the forward bomb bay with a large fiberglass radome mounted under the fuselage to house the APS-20's eight foot by three foot antenna. Provisions were made for two radar operators in the former radioman's station and the fuselage was packed with the radar set, radar data link relay equipment, two VHF radio sets, IFF, and other electronics. The long greenhouse canopy and turret were replaced by a single place cockpit and 'turtle-back' fairing. To improve the Avenger's lateral stability auxiliary tail fins were installed near the tips of the horizontal stabilizers. The XTBM-3W prototype flew for the first time on 5 August 1944 and the Navy authorized immediate conversion of a number of existing TBM-3 and TBM-3E airframes to the TBM-3W configuration.

The intensity of Japanese *Kamikaze* suicide attacks against the Allied fleet off Okinawa added urgency to the conversion program and forty APS-20 radar sets were quickly produced for conversion of a like number of Avengers. By early 1945 operational testing had been completed and aircrew training with the TBM-3W had begun, but the war ended before these TBM-3Ws could be deployed to the Fleet. The operational test program had proven the value of the airborne early warning Avenger and the program continued after the war with the first operational TBM-3W units joining the fleet in May of 1946.

In post-war Carrier Air Groups, the TBM-3Ws were teamed with the TBM-3S anti-submarine strike aircraft in Anti-submarine 'Hunter-Killer' teams. The The TBM-3W was the 'hunter' and could relay radar contacts by data link to both the carrier and the TBM-3S 'killer'. Avengers continued to operate in this role until the mid-1950s when they were replaced by similar versions of the Grumman AF Guardian and Douglas AD Skyraider.

The TBM-3W was the pioneer Airborne Early Warning aircraft which proved the concept and led to today's Grumman E-2C Hawkeye and its ultra-sophisticated electronic capabilities.

The original 'Project Cadillac' XTBM-3W prototype, an extensively modified TBM-3 equipped with an APS-20 radar mounted in the bomb bay. To improve laterial stability auxillery tail fins were installed on the horizontal stabilizers. (Grumman)

Belly Radome

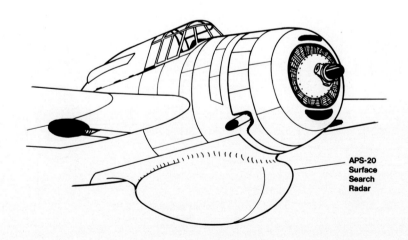

APS-20 Surface Search Radar

A TBM-3W of VX-1 in flight near Naval Air Station Boca Chica, in the Florida Keys during January of 1950. The TBM-3W carried numerous whip antennas, for communications, IFF, and data link transmitters and receivers. The 'turtle-back' fairing was hinged to allow easy access to the electronics behind the pilot's cockpit. (Grumman)

Auxillery Tail Fins

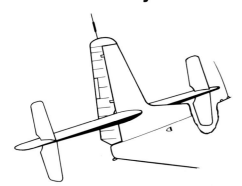

"Turtle-Back" Fairing

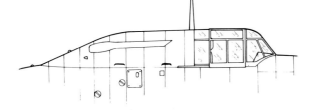

A TBM-3W of VA-4B on USS FRANKLIN D.ROOSEVELT's (CVA-42) port cataput is just seconds away from launch. TMB-3Ws usually operated at some distance from the carrier on standing radar patrols, or teamed with TBM-3S strike aircraft in anti-submarine operations ahead of the carrier. (Grumman)

A number of TBM-3Ws were assigned to naval reserve units. This TBM-3W was flown by LTJG Rooney of VS-833, a Reserve squadron based at NAS Floyd Bennett Field, New York during October of 1954.(Roger Seybel)

US Navy Bombers

"in action"

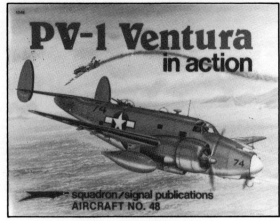

1048 PV1 Ventura

The **IN ACTION** series has been formulated to provide the reader; historian, buff, or modeler, with an in depth and comprehensive study of the subject. Through the use of photographs, scale drawings, perspective drawings, and a concise and authoritative text, a complete understanding of the aircraft's developmental history can be quickly learned from these inexpensive, yet high quality, books. Each contains 50 pages, 50-100 scale drawings, and 4 pages of color, including color covers.

1064 SBD Dauntless

In Color

USN CARRIER AIR UNITS

This mammoth research project presents a detailed examination of the markings and color schemes of the Air Units of the United States Navy, covering both the evolutionary and revolutionary changes that have been made in the camouflage and markings of the fleet's Aircraft Carrier borne air arm with special emphasis on aircraft tail markings.

6160 USN Aircraft Carrier Air Units Vol. 1

6161 USN Aircraft Carrier Air Units Vol. 2

6162 USN Aircraft Carrier Air Units Vol. 3

 **squadron/signal publications, inc.**